365 days,

2day, to

it your

ever...

you do?

A A A B B B C C C D D D

E E F F F G G G H H H H

I I I I J J J K K K L L L L

M M M N N N O O O P P P

Q Q Q R R R S S S T T T

U U U V V V W W W X X X

Y Y Y Y Y Z Z Z

a a a b b b c c c d d d

e e e f f f g g g h h h i

i i j j j k k k l l l m m m

n n n n o o o p p p q q q

r r r r s s s t t t u u u v

v v v v w w w x x x y y y z z

today.....

et me after class and i'll tell yc

, new everything. i wish i were in anoth.

. I wearing that. i HAVE to have that. he likes .

earing friday night? have you ever tried this? what

re not going. y not? u have 2! can I borrow that? PROi

urn it....and then my parents...what was the answer to q

don't like any of my CLOTHES. U said what? I LOVE that m

ou hear that song that goes...oh, I can't stand to eat that! it

gross. She's so sweet, you should meet...no way am I going t

o do that. What was up **My Best Year** then...i f

nuch to do. **For you, all about you & by you.**

Fill in the blanks of your life. I don't know what he's talk

u? I have HOMEWORK 2nite. oh, that sounds so fun. I'm

us. i'm not sure what I'm going to do. what do u think

should say? can u keep a secret? I've been waiting

ey went where? without me? Which looks better?

makes me look older? It's so cool. He's driving

I should sooooo try this...it's so good. how dc

onna be late. This will ruin every hing. Stop

please? that test last week? i can believe wl

, that vas so s pid, why did I say at? nee

i'll t you e thing.. w jeans, r h .

wis' vere i grade t again. no v .

a t' likes . oh. what are you wearing tru

ver tried this? what do u mean you're not going.

can I borrow that? PROMISE i'll return it....and the

at was the answer to question #3? I don't like any of

said what? I LOVE that movie. I'll never listen to her

ou hear that song that goes...oh, I can't stand to eat

my best year

Written and designed by
Mickey & Cheryl Gill

Fine Print Publishing Company
P.O. Box 916401
Longwood, Florida 32971-6401

This book is printed on acid-free paper.
Created in the U.S.A. & Printed in China

ISBN 978-189295143-4

10 9 8 7 6 5 4 3 2 1

coke-or-pepsi.com

If you love
My Best Year,
then check out more

books for you & your friends.
You won't believe what you find out!

Coke or Pepsi?
1000 coke or pepsi questions 2 ask your friends

More Coke or Pepsi?
1000 more coke or pepsi questions 2 ask your friends

Coke or Pepsi? 3
Can you believe it . . .
1000 more coke or pepsi questions 2 ask your friends

coke-or-pepsi.com

Table of Contents

A Little About Me — Pg 8

Pg 11 — A day in the Life of...

Journal Entries — Pg 23

Pg 37 — A Month in the Life of...

Emotional Days — Pg 65

i got bored

LOVE

Pg 81 What Do Your Friends Have to Say?

Pg 100 BFF PHOTOS

Pg 105 The Best and Worst

Pg 116 Save the Best for Last

EXTRA STUFF Pg 119

I HAVE THE POWER TO TAKE ON THE YEAR!

aBOUT me

any TALENTS?

○ not really

○ yeah

_____
_____
_____
_____

BEST FRIEND
IS _____

Fave outfit is:

_____
_____
_____

MOST WORN-OUT
pair of shoes are:
_____

all of my interests
_____
_____
_____
_____
_____
_____
_____
_____

Pets?

○ nope

○ yep

name	kind
name	kind
name	kind

names

I live with

What if

you decided to take off on a lifelong voyage with an alien ship tomorrow – What would you do today, your last day, before u leave?

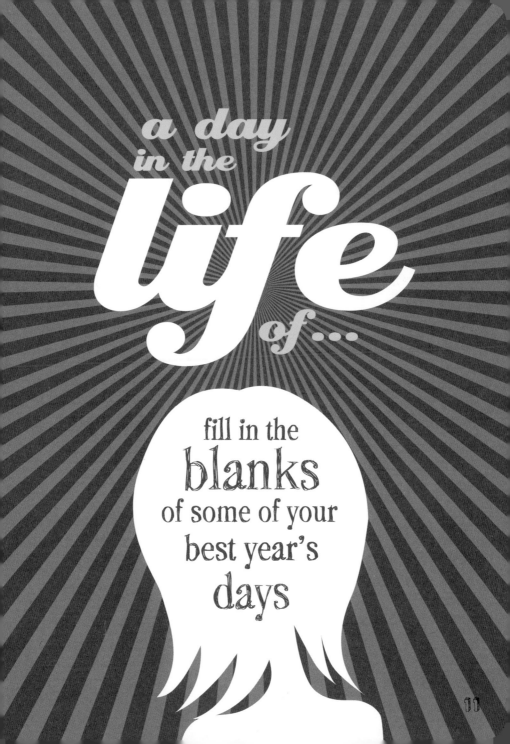

A DAY IN THE LIFE

I woke up @

First person I spoke to was

Last person I spoke to was

hey

L8r

Looking 4ward 2

I'm dreading

DAY & DATE

SOMETHING ○ REALLY COOL
○ awful   ○ hysterical
happened! What was it?

 watched  on TV

_____

I listened to

music

 I had

_____

4 breakfast

2DAY IS A
○ school ○ weekend
○ summer DAY!

I'M FEELING
○ great
○ fine
○ really mad
○ blue
○ so so

in the mood 4
1. ○ cookies ○ chips?
2. ○ sneakers ○ flip-flops?
3. ○ quiet ○ loud?
4. ○ shopping ○ TV?
5. ○ me ○ friend time?

good ○ bad hair day?

TODAY HAS BEEN

Day of the week
_____

Date
_____

2day was like

○ discovering that the dress I've had my 👁 on **SOLD** 10 minutes before I got to the store!!

○ having an amazing-looking 💛 boy notice me smile @ me! **AND**

It would have been an

○ excellent
○ awful
day for my school photo.

Healthiest thing u ate?
_____

Yummiest thing u ate w/ absolutely no nutritional value?

Describe what you're wearing:

LIKE NO OTHER

The Biggest Challenge i Faced was –

- ○ what 2 wear.
- ○ what to do w/friends.
- ○ school. Y? _____
- ○ other _____

Which FRIENDS did you chat with? *about what?*

_____ about _____
name

_____ about _____
name

_____ about _____
name

CURRENTLY, MY BEDROOM IS

- ○ perfectly neat
- ○ an organized wreck – I know where everything is ☺
- ○ a disaster area

toDAY IS tHE 1st

any dreams?

○ not that I remember
○ yes, I dreamed

_____

_____

hmmm, what do u think that meant?

_____

what did u read 2day?

○ back of a cereal box
○ a book – _____
○ does the menu on the TV screen count?
○ other _____

BeSt tHING tHAt HAPPeNeD?

W°RSt tHiNG?

DAY OF the REST OF MY LIFe.

I love my
- old, faded & tattered
- new, hip

jeans

as of _____
day   date

MY FAVeS R:

Friend _____

why? _____

_____

Web site or blog _____

Thing 2 do w/friends _____

Store _____

Word or phrase _____

Color to wear _____

Beverage - cold _____

hot _____

When I'm sad, I
- hide in my room & cry
- call my bffs & cry
- become very quiet
- watch a funny movie

on a scale from 1 to 10 (10 BEING PERFECT) **what would U rate today?**

_____ WHY? _____

17

UR Queen

My friends would describe my **mood** today as

- ○ happy
- ○ depressed
- ○ OK, for the most part
- ○ WORRIED
- ○ other _____
_____

Why do you feel this way?

_____
_____
_____

What national holiday

Holiday name
_____

was the ***first*** thing you thought about when you woke up this morning **?**

_____
_____
_____
_____

Just 4 2day, I would love to
switch places w/_____
travel to _____
not have to _____

# of your **Day**

... would you like to declare?

_____

what u do on this holiday

_____

_____

Last'
thing you thought about before you went to bed **?**

If u could
CHANGE
1 thing about today, what would it be **?**

_____

_____

_____

_____

_____

What kind of girl r you?

A ⚪ lot of ⚪ little make-up?
⚪ dependable ⚪ giving ⚪ crazy friend?
⚪ leader ⚪ follower ⚪ rebel?

IT'S MY

YES!

I WAS bORN

To:

From:

It's _____ & i have ○ BIG PLANS ◎
day of the week
[○ for today
○ another day
○ NO bIG PLANS

THE PLAN

What was the #1 song when u were born?

_____

What is it today?

_____

1 MOVIE, (look it up online)
the year u were born?

1 movie this week?

BIRTHDAY!

___ YEARS AGO ON ___
date

but I can't wait to be ___ so I can _____
age

PRESENTS — what did u get, girl?

_____ from _____
gift   name

_____ from _____
gift   name

_____ from _____
gift   name

_____ from _____
gift   name

_____ from _____
gift   name

BEST GIFT

What did u eat on your B-day?

Get any $?

O no, rats.
O yes. what r u going 2 buy?

What if

you had to choose to attend **1** of these:

☆ an archaeological dig of a Pharaoh's treasures in Egypt (is there really a curse of the mummy?)

☆ a research trip to study the behavior of monkeys in the rainforest (just how **BIG** r the mosquitos?)

☆ a scientific experiment that produces diamonds in a lab (do I get to keep them?)

Which would you choose and **Y**?

Journal Entries

or

thoughts from

me

Here's your **chance** to dig deep & go on & on about who u r, what you love & where you're going.

DEFINING ME

Who r u deep down inside? How would your friends describe u?
How would u describe yourself? Outgoing? Wallflower?
Competitive? Crazy? Brainy?

_____

_____

_____

_____

_____

_____

_____

_____

_____

_____

_____

_____

_____

_____

_____

_____

ENTRY ONE

I ABSOLUTELY LOVE

What do you have a
passion 4? Write down everything
you love – sports, books, friends, food & anything
else that comes to mind.
What makes u crazy for all this stuff?

_____

_____

_____

_____

_____

_____

_____

_____

_____

_____

_____

_____

ENTRY TWO

I love you!

SMILE

25

CAN YOU RELATE?

Who is this
family you live with?
Who do you look like? Who do you act like?
Who do you get and not get along with?
What do you do together?

BEST FRIENDS FOREVER

How, when & where did you meet them?
What do you like about them?
R u so in tune with each other or polar opposites?

_____

_____

_____

_____

_____

_____

_____

_____

_____

_____

_____

_____

_____

ENTRY FOUR

FRIENDS, FOES, TEACHERS & TESTS

How do you like your school? What's it like?
Are you a good student? Like learning or LOVE socializing?
Sports? Clubs?

ENTRY 5

IN MY ROOM

Color of your bedroom? Y did you choose it?
Did you decorate it? What's on the walls?
What's under your bed? How messy is it?
What's your most prized possession in your room?

ENTRY SIX

23

THE PERFECT CRUSH

What are the qualities of the perfect crush?
Funny? Smart? Athletic?
Sensitive? Loves junk food? Honest? Adventurous? Rebel?

ENTRY 7

THEY'RE SO COOL

Who do you admire or think is really cool?
What is it about them? What traits
do they have that you wished you did?
Adult, BFF, family member, athlete, celebrity?

ENTRY 8

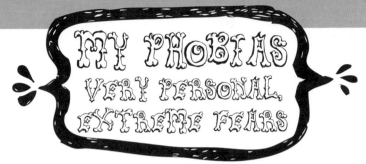

MY PHOBIAS
VERY PERSONAL, EXTREME FEARS

Spiders, roaches, or snakes? Think bigger too — tests,
speaking in front of a crowd, getting in trouble, going to parties.
What are you frightened of?
Something you're scared of that would surprise most people?

_____

_____

_____

_____

_____

_____

_____

_____

_____

_____

_____

_____

ENTRY 9

FUTURE FLASH

What do you think you'll be
doing in 15 years? School?
Will you be at your dream job?
Marriage? Children? Where will you live?

_____

_____

_____

_____

_____

_____

_____

_____

_____

_____

_____

_____

_____

ENTRY TEN

33

MY VERY

FAVORITE PLACE

Ever visit the most amazing place? What made it beautiful? Scenery? People? Or, maybe your special place is just a place to hang out with friends in town or somewhere to be alone. What makes it cool? What do you do there?

_____

_____

_____

_____

_____

_____

_____

_____

_____

_____

_____

_____

_____

_____

_____

ENTRY 11

MOUNTAINS

MY WORLD, JUST BETTER

If you could change something in your world, what would it be?
Would looks, popularity & money mean nothing in a perfect world?
Would people love more? Or would your change be more simple –
like a 4-day school week?

What if

you **won** $1,000,000 & had to use it up in **one** day?

How would u spend it?
- ☆ Buy a posh mansion
- ☆ Give it all to charity
- ☆ Share it with family and friends
- ☆ other

Why did u choose that?

A
month in the
life
of...

Answer
thought-provoking
questions
that follow you
through school,
vacation & all
4 seasons.

MONTH

this month has been

month _____

this month has been
- ○ a breeze
- ○ cool
- ○ a little stinky
- ○ really hard

Describe the last **4** weeks
in **5** lines or less

_____
_____
_____
_____

Crush Alert

- ○ he doesn't know i'm alive.
- ○ he knows i'm alive . . . that's it!
- ○ i THINK he likes me?
- ○ no crush in sight!

what's been going on with u & your bff?

○ good stuff   ○ awfulness   ○ what bff?

details. . .

**What 1 item from your wardrobe
have U been wearing the most lately?**

_____

Something that surprised you?

_____
_____

ONE

1

R U feeling
- ○ hopeful
- ○ confused?

y? _____
_____
_____

- ○ milk chocolate
- ○ dark chocolate
- ○ white chocolate

sometimes i dream about . . .
- ○ being older
- ○ leading a completely different life
- ○ what it would be like to _____
_____
_____
_____

_____ **was** _____
Month   Number of days in month

of _____
                    Adjective to describe your month

In fact, if this month were a movie, it would be a:

☐ romantic comedy   ☐ drama   ☐ horror   ☐ thriller!   ☐ boring documentary

Y? do tell

Who would be your cast of characters?
(Friends, family, etc. Who would win for best dramatic performance?)

Nothing's New...

My whole  is changing

what hasn't changed since last month?

what's different this month from last?

What's been on your mind? What are you always thinking about?

How does your heart feel?

month no.3

○ butterfly
○ dragonfly
○ other?_____

month of

_____

What's your average temp?
○ Hot! i've been mad
○ Cold... i've been sad
○ Pretty nice, things r good

What's affecting your temp?_____

this month, i VOW to break the habit of

_____

CRUSH ALERT!
○ Something   ○ Nothing

NEW has developed! ↙

○ rainy   ○ sunny   ○ snowy days r the best!

coolest thing u did this month?

fave radio station?
(name & call letters)

Heard a new song u must HAVE?
○ **Nah** music scene stinks —
○ **Yeah**   artist _____
                    song _____

fave T.V. show

OH The Pain

Anyone hurt your feelings lately?
○ **No**   ○ **Yes**
what happened?

Have u hurt anyone's feelings lately?
○ **No**   ○ **Yes**
what happened?

43

the 4th month

_____ **of**
month

_____ **will**
year

**never,
ever, happen
again, and I'm**

○ ok with that
○ kinda sad really
○ SO RELIEVED!

Y·····▲ _____
_____
_____

what's
your motto
for this month?

no pet?
make 1 up.

If your pet
could talk, what would
he or she say about what's
really going on with u?

_____
_____
_____
_____
_____
_____
_____
_____

R u really
going to
wear that?

week 1

What's going on at home?

_____
_____
_____

i feel like
- ⚪ a castaway on a desert island
- ⚪ a hamster running on 1 of those circular track thingies
- ⚪ a fairy godmother is taking care of me

week 2

What's going on w/ friends?

_____
_____
_____

my friends r
- ⚪ great listeners & so cool
- ⚪ slowly slipping away
- ⚪ changing right now . . . making **new** ones! YEAH!

week 3

Anyone super nice to you? What did he or she do?

_____
_____
_____

No? Sorry ° °

If this week were a FRENCH perfume, it would be called eau de
- ⚪ lovely
- ⚪ crazy
- ⚪ stink!
- ⚪ parfait (perfect)

week 4

Anything going on with boys, crushes, etc?

_____
_____
_____

If u could push DELETE & wipe out 1 day this week, which would it be?

_____
day of the week

Y? _____
_____

Did you learn anything new this month?

Yeah you did! Think about it. Close your eyes really tight and concentrate. It works.

⚪ no ⚪ yes _____
_____

47

I'm so **blue** 'cause . . .

I like ○ I best friend ○ a group of good friends

If this month were a color, what would it be?

I'M RED HOT MAD ABOUT . . .

Not Black & White

I've been so confused about . . .

FIRE & ICE

Who have U not been getting along with lately? Why?

I'm GREEN with envy because . . .

It's the month of

Spending most of my time
- ○ doing homework
- ○ hanging out with friends
- ○ doing nothing! I'm bored!
- ○ _____

Who would U luv 2 trade places with? _____

Why?

If U saw a falling ★, what would U wish 4?

○ Shopping ○ Talking to a friend
○ Scarfing my fave junk food
can solve almost anything!

○ daisies ○ wildflowers ○ roses?

Friends would say my
○ head's in the clouds
○ feet r planted on the ground

Month number five

47

Month #6

_____

It's the month

of _____

& i'm ○ too busy
○ dreaming of _____
○ pretty happy really

Are you more
● seNse
● seNsibility?

Have u heard anything
lately that surprised **you?**
○ no ○ yes
_____
_____
_____

○ iNdecisive
○ very decisive?

HeaD vs. HeaRt

Having trouble making a decision because your heart feels 1
way but your head says something else? ○ no ○ yes

 _____
_____

ANy bRilliaNt IdeaS?

It doesn't have to be the Next new energy source – just an idea of any kind.

○ not really, but I've been thinking about _____

_____

○ yes, & my idea is _____

_____

I cried my 👁 s out oVer _____

_____

Words i
said that I wish I could take back

_____

_____

_____

Send out any text messages that u shouldn't have?

○ I don't think so
○ rats ... yes! ↓

_____

_____

_____

_____

Crush aleRt

What do your friends think of your crush?

○ don't like him   ○ they adore him too!

○ they don't know about him

○ think we are a perfect match

49

MY BFFS & I have been mostly talking about
○ school ○ sports ○ clothes
○ boys ○ other _____

Any recent "friendly" dramas?
○ nah, not really ○ oh, yeah!

Details _____
_____
_____

R U a problem ○ solver ○ maker
○ wish-awayer?

BIGGEST prob in your life →

3 things you have no control of in your life?
1 _____
2 _____
3 _____

1 thing U can change about your life?
_____

secrets:
○ my lips are sealed!
○ not so good @ keeping
○ hate them!

_____
month

5 things U LOVE
about your life right now

Better to have
○ loved & lost
○ never loved at all

1 _____
2 _____
3 _____
4 _____
5 _____

○ blue ○ pink ○ yellow ○ green?

○ math ○ science
○ english ○ history
○ other
_____

What do you spend most of your time doing?

51

The month of _____

ha

I've been ____
of my tim____

Something ____
laughed ____

My main mode____
has been ____

The 1 thing my
friends & I love is
_____

My bffs & I hate ____

mo.

Ask your bffs who they think has the best hair out of the girls u know

Ever judged someone based on hair?

○ yes, i'm awful!

○ no way, that's rude!

s been all about

(List 5 things you've been busy doing)

pending most
anging out with

_____

& your friends
eally hard about –

_____

f chatting
o on the phone
o im
o live

1. _____
2. _____
3. _____
4. _____
5. _____

Been in trouble lately?
O no, been an angel
O yeah. What did u do? _____

_____

_____

Grounded?
O nah O yeah
what were u
forbidden to do?

_____

_____

my hair is...

O OK, some days
O great enough for a
shampoo commercial

O always my biggest beauty prob! 53

Baby,

What's the coolest thing about u RIGHT NOW?

_____

I'M HAPPIEST
- HANGING W/FRIENDS
- WHEN I GET TIME ALONE
- WHEN I GET TO SNACK ON

_____

- OTHER

What R the ingredients of the ultimate sundae?

_____

WHAT
MAKES
YOU
THINK
THAT?

_____

I TRULY BELIEVE THE ADULTS IN MY LIFE
- R WISER & MORE EXPERIENCED THAN ME
- DON'T ACTUALLY HAVE A CLUE

it's the month of

1ST
If you could try something new this month, what would it be?

_____
_____

7TH
7 people U talked to 2day

16TH
TODAY WAS AS GOOD AS
- RAW COOKIE DOUGH
- BRUSSELS SPROUTS
- OTHER _____

What happened?

_____
_____
_____

WHAT R U DYING TO DO 2DAY?

_____
_____
_____

↑ You pick a date

23RD
- I'm ready to take on the world!
- I want to crawl in a hole and hide.

Why? _____

crush alert
All the details, please

Month number and counting

ode to _____

This month finds me

_____.
activity u usually do during this month

As _____
current fave singer/band

sings loudly in the background, I think about

_____
something legal your parents won't let u do

But alas, I cannot. So, I

_____ & dream
chore you need to do

about some day being able to
do whatever I want.

Something u wish u could make appear with the wave of a magic wand:

month ten

My fave thing in my room is

_____

Last long talk with a family member was with

_____
family member

about

_____
topic

_____

I wish I could see

_____

from my bedroom window.

I AM A TOTAL

○ free bird
○ rule follower
○ well-balanced girl

I've been reading

○ magazines

_____
which ones?

_____

○ txt messages mainly
○ the book _____

for ○ school ○ fun

when **talking** to friends, I

○ am sometimes guilty of exaggerating
○ stick to the facts
○ usually don't share enough details

What will you remember most about this month?

_____

My shoe size is

BESIDES UNDER-WEAR!→

What item of clothing would u never let a BFF borrow?

_____
month

MY COOLEST SHOES R MY

no.
XI

My toes r:
- nude
- painted _____
  color
- chipped

How many Pairs
of shoes do U own?
- not enough! - just enough!
- way too many-how many?

58

BEST

The 3 coolest things about my #1 bff r:

New song I've heard is _____
by _____

1 _____
2 _____
3 _____

Funniest video
😆 I've seen lately:
_____
_____

_____

WHAT's
the weirdest
thing about
_____
_____ **YOU** ?
_____

Something u did this month
that u MAY never do again
in your life?

**Can u finish your
friends' sentences?**
○ yes ○ no

Fave t-shirt in your closet?

Draw your yeas with words on a tricked-out tee. ⌐

How many ↑ pairs of jeans do u own?

it's ^{almost} 1 year later...

lips
- ○ gloss
- ○ chapstick
- ○ nothing

_____ month

i spend most of my

Saturdays & *Sundays*

_____
whatever you do on the weekends

check all that apply
roller coaster
- ○ front seat
- ○ back seat
- ○ screaming!
- ○ arms in the air
- ○ eyes closed
- ○ NEVER!

crush alert
I'm
- ○ still dreaming & hoping
- ○ in love
- ○ in like
- ○ broken

Tattoos R so ○ cool ○ gross

1 thing I'd like to change about the world

_____
_____
_____
_____

What's the best thing a bff has done 4 u recently? _____
_____

63

the Summer of

_____ year

Run out of room for all the *Juicy* details of your summer break? Here u go!

What did you do on the last day of school?

_____

How 'bout the **1ST** day of summer?

Summer school? ○ no ○ yes-what did you take?

_____

Time u usually rolled out of bed?

How late did u stay up?

Meet any **BOYS?** ○ nah ○ yeah

details?

62

I ○ loved summer! ○ actually missed school

Go to any cool
parties?
○ nope, not really
○ yep _____
_____

Go on *vacation?*
○ no, drag ○ yes. Where?
_____
What did you do? _____
_____

○ Bikini ○ Shorts & a tee
○ Other_____
was my summer
uniform

what did u do on the
last day of summer?

_____
_____

What if

you could live anywhere else in the world for **1** year—

where would you live & why?

MERHABA Bonjour JAMBO

Hallo

Aloha Hey

Ciao HOLA

Sa-wa dee kah

emotional days

for all those
fab days,
sad days &
all around bad days —
write down just
how cool (or rotten)
each second was . . .

My most absolutely fabulous days

date _____

_____
_____
_____
_____

date _____

_____
_____
_____
_____

ever have those days when you think, "WOW, i really had a cool day."? write it down so you don't forget the details.

date

date

date

These were the Saddest days ever

Date _____

_____

_____

_____

_____

Date _____

_____

_____

_____

_____

_____

Date _____

_____

_____

_____

_____

you're so mad. you're sad. you lost a friend, a pet, or just a game.
your heart is broken. things are just unfair. someone said awful
things about you. you feel like you'll never smile again . . .

you bawled your **eyes** out & now they're red & puffy, your nose is running, the words leaving your mouth are completely incoherent because you can barely **breathe** & all you can **taste** is salt (saline in your tears) . . . **try** to write down what happened . . . sometimes it helps.

Date _____

_____

_____

_____

_____

_____

Date _____

_____

_____

_____

_____

_____

Date _____

_____

_____

_____

_____

_____

i'm MAD!
DAYS

Date

_____
_____
_____
_____

Date

_____
_____
_____
_____

Date

_____
_____
_____
_____

Scream across these pages. What made you want to **YELL** at the top of your lungs?

Date _____
_____
_____
_____
_____

Date _____
_____
_____
_____
_____

i can't talk about it any more.

Date _____
_____
_____
_____
_____

the days that made u say

"i've never been so

Embarrassed

in all my life!"

Date _____

_____
_____
_____
_____

Date _____

_____
_____
_____
_____
_____

Date _____

_____
_____
_____
_____
_____

ugh...

You remember them **Forever**, unfortunately, but somehow you survive. Toilet paper on the shoe, tripping & falling, zipper down. Keep track of the awful (and sometimes even funny) events of your year.

Date

_____
_____
_____
_____

Date

_____
_____
_____
_____

Date

_____
_____
_____
_____

humiliation

you're in a MOOD Qays

Date

_____
_____
_____
_____

Date

_____
_____
_____
_____

Date

_____
_____
_____

Sweet one moment, mean the next, sweet again.
RUDE, even to people you love. Friends are like
"what's up?" U don't even know y you're in a fu
You'll snap out of it . . . eventually.
Until then, scribble some thoughts
down here.

Date

_____
_____
_____
_____

Date

_____
_____
_____
_____

Date

_____
_____
_____
_____

"I'm in Love or at least Like."

days

Date
_____
_____
_____
_____

Date
_____
_____
_____
_____

pour your heart out

pulse quickens. Giggling at everything your crush says, even when it's not that funny. Notebook overflowing with heart doodles. Then 1 day something happens & ur *crushin'* over someone else.

Date _____

_____
_____
_____
_____
_____

Date _____

_____
_____
_____
_____
_____

Date _____

_____
_____
_____
_____

it's something
u never say
out loud, but you feel it
some days...
you're Jealous

date

_____
_____
_____
_____
_____

date

_____
_____
_____
_____
_____

date

_____
_____
_____
_____
_____

_____
_____
_____
_____
_____
_____

_____
_____
_____
_____
_____
_____

_____
_____
_____
_____
_____
_____
_____

wishing
u could be that
smart, pretty,
cool...
i want what they
have ... a nasty
feeling that
makes u think
or say mean
things. put
your feelings
on paper instead
& think about
the "BEST"
things in YOUR
LIFE.

What if

you could be any animal
except a human –
Which would you choose?

O Lion O in the wild O in a zoo

O Horse O in the wild O on a farm

O Wild bird What kind?

O Pet dog What kind?

O Other

what do *your* friends have to say?

You have
1 year
to ask all of your
bffs over
100
questions

Name _____

1. **3** words your friends use to describe u?

_____ _____ _____

2. What was your last dream about? _____

Doughnut flavor? _____
Store @ the mall? _____
Movie? _____

3. ◯ Creamy ◯ Crunchy peanut butter?   4. ◯ Morning glory ◯ Night owl?

5. ◯ Great ◯ OK ◯ Not so hot student?

6. What did u watch on TV last night? _____

7. Most popular color in your closet? _____

8. Famous person u would trade places w/? _____

9. Best personality trait? _____

10. Worst personality trait? _____

11. ◯ High fashion ◯ Totally casual?   12. ◯ Social butterfly ◯ Wallflower?

13. ◯ Meat Eater ◯ Vegetarian ◯ Vegan? Why? _____

14. What color are your toes painted?

_____

15. Who do u want to see in concert?

_____

Name _____

1. Word or phrase u say a lot?

2. How would u describe yourself?

3. What do you do when ur upset?

4. ◯ Brownies ◯ Chocolate chip cookies?

5. ◯ Small purse   ◯ Giant bag?

6. ◯ Professional manicure ◯ Do-it-yourself nails ◯ Au naturelle?

7. Write papers ◯ in advance ◯ a few days before ◯ the night before?

8. Usually have ◯ bad ◯ so-so ◯ good hair days?

9. What's your typical Saturday? _____

10. **2** words to describe boys: _____   _____

11. Been in a play? ◯ No ◯ Yes. What was your part?_____

12. ◯ Small talk ◯ Deep conversation? Y? _____

13. Fries: ◯ shoestring ◯ crinkle cut ◯ steak ◯ waffle

14. Can u use chopsticks? ◯ Yes ◯ No

15. How would u spend $1,000 in 1 day? _____

Ice cream flavor? _____
Magazine? _____
Song? _____

83

Name _____

1. Who should play u in a movie version of your life? _____

2. Best costume you've ever worn? _____

3. Movie you can watch again & again? _____

4. Ever had stitches? ○ No ○ Yes. Y? _____

FAVES

Cookie? _____

Clothing Brand? _____

TV Show? _____

5. ○ Make quick decisions ○ Think about it ○ Avoid making decisions?

6. I know a lot about _____

7. ○ Leader ○ Follower ○ Somewhere in between?

8. When ur mad, do u ○ yell ○ cry ○ get quiet?

9. Ever been on TV? ○ No ○ Yes. What 4?

10. ○ TV ○ Book ○ Online?

11. How would your parents describe u?

12. Best thing about school?

13. Who do u trust w/ the deep stuff?

14. Best snack to nosh on? _____

15. **1** word to describe girls: _____

Name _____

1. ◯ Bagel ◯ Doughnut ◯ Croissant ◯ Cinnamon roll?

2. ◯ Off-the-charts G.P.A. ◯ Spending time w/ crush for 1 year?

3. ◯ Big Mac ◯ Whopper

4. I know absolutely nothing about _____

5. Best kind of dog? _____

6. Last movie u saw? _____

7. **4** things u love to do: _____ _____ _____ _____

Kind of pizza? _____

School subject? _____

Singer? _____

FAVES

8. Fallen down in public? ◯ No ◯ Yes. What happened? _____

9. ◯ Taco ◯ Burrito ◯ Enchilada ◯ Fajita?

10. ◯ Tanning oil ◯ Faux tan ◯ Sunscreen?

11. ◯ Island cabana ◯ European castle ◯ Safari tent ◯ Ski lodge?

12. Best season & Y? _____

13. What makes u crazy? _____

14. Favorite place you've visited? _____

15. Something u luv that most people hate? _____

Name _____

1. Ever surfed? ○ No ○ Yes. Which coast?

2. ○ Clean freak ○ Total slob?

3. What do u like on your burger?

4. Most embarrassing moment ever was _____

5. What super sense would u choose? _____

Beverage? _____

Cake? _____

Actor? _____

FAVES

6. **3** places you'd luv to visit: _____ _____ _____

7. Rules should be ○ followed ○ used as guidelines ○ broken?

8. Nails: ○ Painted ○ Chipped ○ Faux ○ Bitten?

9. Something legal ur addicted 2? _____

10. What scares you the most? _____

11. Best book you've ever read? _____

12. R u ○ introverted ○ extroverted ○ somewhere in the middle?

13. ○ Dog ○ Cat ○ Other _____ person?

14. ○ Waffle cone ○ Sugar cone ○ Cup?

15. Best type of movie: ○ Romance ○ Comedy ○ Scary ○ Action

Name _____

1. Best band since u were born? _____

2. First word u said? _____

3. **4** words 2 describe u: _____ _____ _____ _____

Smoothie? _____

Commercial? _____

Actress? _____

FAVES

4. ◯ Dreamer ◯ Doer?

5. ◯ Go with the flow ◯ Stick to a routine?

6. ◯ Gold ◯ Silver ◯ Other _____ ?

7. I lose track of time when I _____

8. Time travel forward 2 _____

9. Time travel back 2 _____

10. Worst fashion mistake you've ever made? _____

11. Like being in the spotlight? ◯ But of course ◯ Sometimes ◯ Never!

12. Ever won anything? ◯ No ◯ Yes. What? _____

13. Which would u be? ◯ Star ◯ Supporting star ◯ Director ◯ Set designer

14. Which would u try? ◯ Sky diving ◯ Rappelling ◯ Scuba diving?

15. Fave holiday? _____ Y? _____

Name _____

1. **3** words your friends use to describe u?

_____ _____ _____

2. What was your last dream about? _____

Doughnut flavor? _____
Store @ the mall? _____
Movie? _____

FAVES

3. ○ Creamy ○ Crunchy peanut butter? 4. ○ Morning glory ○ Night owl?

5. ○ Great ○ OK ○ Not so hot student?

6. What did u watch on TV last night? _____

7. Most popular color in your closet? _____

8. Famous person u would trade places w/? _____

9. Best personality trait? _____

10. Worst personality trait? _____

11. ○ High fashion ○ Totally casual? 12. ○ Social butterfly ○ Wallflower?

13. ○ Meat Eater ○ Vegetarian ○ Vegan? Why? _____

14. What color are your toes painted?

_____

15. Who do u want to see in concert?

_____

Name _____

1. Word or phrase u say a lot? _____

2. How would u describe yourself? _____

3. What do you do when ur upset? _____

4. ◯ Brownies ◯ Chocolate chip cookies?

5. ◯ Small purse ◯ Giant bag?

6. ◯ Professional manicure ◯ Do-it-yourself nails ◯ Au naturelle?

7. Write papers ◯ in advance ◯ a few days before ◯ the night before?

8. Usually have ◯ bad ◯ so-so ◯ good hair days?

9. What's your typical Saturday? _____

10. **2** words to describe boys: _____ _____

11. Been in a play? ◯ No ◯ Yes. What was your part?_____

12. ◯ Small talk ◯ Deep conversation? Y? _____

13. Fries: ◯ shoestring ◯ crinkle cut ◯ steak ◯ waffle

14. Can u use chopsticks? ◯ Yes ◯ No

15. How would u spend $1,000 in 1 day? _____

Ice cream flavor? _____
Magazine? _____
Song? _____

FAVES

Name _____

1. Who should play u in a movie version of your life? _____

2. Best costume you've ever worn? _____

3. Movie you can watch again & again? _____

4. Ever had stitches? ○ No ○ Yes. Y? _____

Cookie? _____

Clothing Brand? _____

TV Show? _____

FAVES

5. ○ Make quick decisions ○ Think about it ○ Avoid making decisions?

6. I know a lot about _____

7. ○ Leader ○ Follower ○ Somewhere in between?

8. When ur mad, do u ○ yell ○ cry ○ get quiet?

9. Ever been on TV? ○ No ○ Yes. What 4? _____

10. ○ TV ○ Book ○ Online?

11. How would your parents describe u?

12. Best thing about school?

13. Who do u trust w/ the deep stuff?

14. Best snack to nosh on? _____

15. 1 word to describe girls: _____

90

Name _____

1. ◯ Bagel ◯ Doughnut ◯ Croissant ◯ Cinnamon roll?

2. ◯ Off-the-charts G.P.A. ◯ Spending time w/ crush for 1 year?

3. ◯ Big Mac ◯ Whopper

4. I know absolutely nothing about _____

5. Best kind of dog? _____

6. Last movie u saw? _____

7. **4** things u love to do: _____ _____ _____ _____

Kind of pizza? _____
School subject? _____
Singer? _____

FAVES

8. Fallen down in public? ◯ No ◯ Yes. What happened? _____

9. ◯ Taco ◯ Burrito ◯ Enchilada ◯ Fajita?

10. ◯ Tanning oil ◯ Faux tan ◯ Sunscreen?

11. ◯ Island cabana ◯ European castle ◯ Safari tent ◯ Ski lodge?

12. Best season & Y? _____

13. What makes u crazy? _____

14. Favorite place you've visited? _____

15. Something u luv that most people hate? _____

Name _____

1. Ever surfed? ○ No ○ Yes. Which coast?

2. ○ Clean freak ○ Total slob?

3. What do u like on your burger?

4. Most embarrassing moment ever was _____

5. What super sense would u choose? _____

Beverage? _____
Cake? _____
Actor? _____

FAVES

6. **3** places you'd luv to visit: _____ _____ _____

7. Rules should be ○ followed ○ used as guidelines ○ broken?

8. Nails: ○ Painted ○ Chipped ○ Faux ○ Bitten?

9. Something legal ur addicted 2? _____

10. What scares you the most? _____

11. Best book you've ever read? _____

12. R u ○ introverted ○ extroverted ○ somewhere in the middle?

13. ○ Dog ○ Cat ○ Other _____ person?

14. ○ Waffle cone ○ Sugar cone ○ Cup?

15. Best type of movie: ○ Romance ○ Comedy ○ Scary ○ Action

Name _____

1. Best band since u were born? _____

2. First word u said? _____

3. **4** words 2 describe u: _____ _____ _____ _____

Smoothie? _____

Commercial? _____

Actress? _____

FAVES

4. ○ Dreamer   ○ Doer?

5. ○ Go with the flow   ○ Stick to a routine?

6. ○ Gold   ○ Silver   ○ Other_____?

7. I lose track of time when I _____

8. Time travel forward 2 _____

9. Time travel back 2 _____

10. Worst fashion mistake you've ever made? _____

11. Like being in the spotlight? ○ But of course   ○ Sometimes   ○ Never!

12. Ever won anything? ○ No   ○ Yes. What?_____

13. Which would u be? ○ Star   ○ Supporting star   ○ Director   ○ Set designer

14. Which would u try? ○ Sky diving   ○ Rappelling   ○ Scuba diving?

15. Fave holiday? _____Y? _____

Name _____

1. **3** words your friends use to describe u?

_____ _____ _____

2. What was your last dream about? _____

Doughnut flavor? _____
Store @ the mall? _____
Movie? _____

FAVES

3. ○ Creamy ○ Crunchy peanut butter?   4. ○ Morning glory ○ Night owl?

5. ○ Great ○ OK ○ Not so hot student?

6. What did u watch on TV last night? _____

7. Most popular color in your closet? _____

8. Famous person u would trade places w/? _____

9. Best personality trait? _____

10. Worst personality trait? _____

11. ○ High fashion ○ Totally casual?   12. ○ Social butterfly ○ Wallflower?

13. ○ Meat Eater ○ Vegetarian ○ Vegan? Why? _____

14. What color are your toes painted?

_____

15. Who do u want to see
in concert?

_____

Name _____

1. Word or phrase u say a lot? _____

2. How would u describe yourself? _____

3. What do you do when ur upset? _____

4. ⭕ Brownies ⭕ Chocolate chip cookies?

5. ⭕ Small purse ⭕ Giant bag?

6. ⭕ Professional manicure ⭕ Do-it-yourself nails ⭕ Au naturelle?

7. Write papers ⭕ in advance ⭕ a few days before ⭕ the night before?

8. Usually have ⭕ bad ⭕ so-so ⭕ good hair days?

9. What's your typical Saturday? _____

10. **2** words to describe boys: _____ _____

11. Been in a play? ⭕ No ⭕ Yes. What was your part?_____

12. ⭕ Small talk ⭕ Deep conversation? Y? _____

13. Fries: ⭕ shoestring ⭕ crinkle cut ⭕ steak ⭕ waffle

14. Can u use chopsticks? ⭕ Yes ⭕ No

15. How would u spend $1,000 in 1 day? _____

Ice cream flavor? _____
Magazine? _____
Song? _____

FAVeS

Name _____

1. Who should play u in a movie version of your life? _____

2. Best costume you've ever worn? _____

3. Movie you can watch again & again? _____

4. Ever had stitches? ◯ No ◯ Yes. Y? _____

FAVES

Cookie? _____

Clothing Brand? _____

TV Show? _____

5. ◯ Make quick decisions ◯ Think about it ◯ Avoid making decisions?

6. I know a lot about _____

7. ◯ Leader ◯ Follower ◯ Somewhere in between?

8. When ur mad, do u ◯ yell ◯ cry ◯ get quiet?

9. Ever been on TV? ◯ No ◯ Yes. What 4? _____

10. ◯ TV ◯ Book ◯ Online?

11. How would your parents describe u?

12. Best thing about school?

13. Who do u trust w/ the deep stuff?

14. Best snack to nosh on? _____

15. 1 word to describe girls: _____

96

Name _____

1. ⚪ Bagel   ⚪ Doughnut   ⚪ Croissant   ⚪ Cinnamon roll?

2. ⚪ Off-the-charts G.P.A.   ⚪ Spending time w/ crush for 1 year?

3. ⚪ Big Mac   ⚪ Whopper

4. I know absolutely nothing about _____

5. Best kind of dog? _____

6. Last movie u saw? _____

7. **4** things u love to do: _____ _____ _____ _____

Kind of pizza? _____

School subject? _____

Singer? _____

FAVES

8. Fallen down in public?   ⚪ No   ⚪ Yes. What happened? _____

9. ⚪ Taco   ⚪ Burrito   ⚪ Enchilada   ⚪ Fajita?

10. ⚪ Tanning oil   ⚪ Faux tan   ⚪ Sunscreen?

11. ⚪ Island cabana   ⚪ European castle   ⚪ Safari tent   ⚪ Ski lodge?

12. Best season & Y? _____

13. What makes u crazy? _____

14. Favorite place you've visited? _____

15. Something u luv that most people hate? _____

Name _____

1. Ever surfed? ○ No ○ Yes. Which coast?

2. ○ Clean freak ○ Total slob?

3. What do u like on your burger?

4. Most embarrassing moment ever was _____

5. What super sense would u choose? _____

Beverage? _____
Cake? _____
Actor? _____

FAVES

6. **3** places you'd luv to visit: _____ _____ _____

7. Rules should be ○ followed ○ used as guidelines ○ broken?

8. Nails: ○ Painted ○ Chipped ○ Faux ○ Bitten?

9. Something legal ur addicted 2? _____

10. What scares you the most? _____

11. Best book you've ever read? _____

12. R u ○ introverted ○ extroverted ○ somewhere in the middle?

13. ○ Dog ○ Cat ○ Other _____ person?

14. ○ Waffle cone ○ Sugar cone ○ Cup?

15. Best type of movie: ○ Romance ○ Comedy ○ Scary ○ Action

Name _____

1. Best band since u were born? _____

2. First word u said? _____

3. **4** words 2 describe u: _____ _____ _____ _____

Smoothie? _____
Commercial? _____
Actress? _____

FAVES

4. ◯ Dreamer ◯ Doer?

5. ◯ Go with the flow ◯ Stick to a routine?

6. ◯ Gold ◯ Silver ◯ Other _____?

7. I lose track of time when I _____

8. Time travel forward 2 _____

9. Time travel back 2 _____

10. Worst fashion mistake you've ever made? _____

11. Like being in the spotlight? ◯ But of course ◯ Sometimes ◯ Never!

12. Ever won anything? ◯ No ◯ Yes. What? _____

13. Which would u be? ◯ Star ◯ Supporting star ◯ Director ◯ Set designer

14. Which would u try? ◯ Sky diving ◯ Rappelling ◯ Scuba diving?

15. Fave holiday? _____ Y? _____

My Friends in _____

Your friend photo here

First _____

Middle _____

Last _____

_____
1 word to describe your friend

Fave thing 2 do together _____

_____

How long have you been friends? _____

Your friend photo here

First _____

Middle _____

Last _____

_____
1 word to describe your friend

Fave thing 2 do together _____

_____

How long have you been friends? _____

Your
friend
photo
here

First _____

Middle _____

Last _____

_____
I word to describe your friend

Fave thing 2 do together _____

_____

How long have you been friends? _____

Your
friend
photo
here

First _____

Middle _____

Last _____

_____
I word to describe your friend

Fave thing 2 do together _____

_____

How long have you been friends? _____

My Friends in _____
year

First _____

Middle _____

Last _____

_____
1 word to describe your friend

Fave thing 2 do together _____

_____

How long have you been friends? _____

Your friend photo here

First _____

Middle _____

Last _____

_____
1 word to describe your friend

Fave thing 2 do together _____

_____

How long have you been friends? _____

Your friend photo here

Your friend photo here

First _____

Middle _____

Last _____

_____
I word to describe your friend

Fave thing 2 do together _____

_____

How long have you been friends? _____

Your friend photo here

First _____

Middle _____

Last _____

_____
I word to describe your friend

Fave thing 2 do together _____

_____

How long have you been friends? _____

What if

you had just returned from
being stranded on a
                    desert island—

Who's the first person
you'd want to see?

What's the first thing you'd
want to do?

What's the first thing you'd
want to eat?

The Best & Worst

It was the **coolest** song. That was an awful class! Keep track of your **top 10 faves** (& not so faves) here.

 song _____ _____
title   artist

 IS IT YOUR FAVE?

my top 10 songs of ____ ____ ____ ____
year

2 _____
title
_____
artist

3 _____
title
_____
artist

4 _____
title
_____
artist

5 _____
title
_____
artist

6 _____
title
_____
artist

7 _____
title
_____
artist

8 _____
title
_____
artist

9 _____
title
_____
artist

10 _____
title
_____
artist

LOUD

LYRICS TO THE
BEST song of the YEAR
(in my humble opinion)

song title _____ _____ artist

_____

_____

_____

_____

_____

_____

_____

_____

_____

i
thought
they were
singing

_____

but they
are really
saying

_____

Don't know all the words? Check online.
Were U surprised @ some of the words?
O Yeah   O Nah, not really

Watch the Oscars? ○ *yes* ○ *no*

Who won Best Actor?...................................

Best Actress?..

How 'bout movie?.......................................

Who wore the best gown?
....

What movie (of all time) has the best kiss?

The

MOVIE

Starring _____

in _____
year
_____

what was the plot? _____

Any other movie tie with your 1st place choice?

○ *no* ○ *yes* ▸ ....

Fave movie actor of ●●●● was ....
year

Fave movie actress was ....

The rest of my top 10 movies!

2   3   4   5

108

Tastiest cinematic food is
○ popcorn ○ candy ....
                                    kind
                    ○ other ....
○ plain ○ buttered?

How 'bout beverage? ....

Best

I SAW

was _____
_____
_____
_____

How much does a movie cost u?

Who do you usually see movies with? ....

Put your feet up on the chair in front of u? ○ no, rude!
                                            ○ yeah, sorry ☹

Write down a great movie line here

7   8   9   10

Tv Hotties

Most beautiful actress? _____

Best looking actor? _____

Show u would
like to appear on?
_____

I would be
so incredibly upset
if _____
name of show
ever went off the air!

What was the story line this year?

_____
_____
_____

Do you follow the lives of your favorite tv stars?

○ of course! ○ not really

Best tv actor of ○○○○○ is most definitely _____
year
& the best actress is _____

My absolute favorite Top Ten TV shows of

Do U record it & watch later?
○ nope ○ yep

Who is in it?

_____
names
_____
_____
_____
_____

_____
Year

1 _____
name

two _____
name

three _____
name

four _____
name

five _____
name

six _____
name

seven _____
name

eight _____
name

I can hardly wait until
_____ _____
day of the week   time
when it's on!

nine _____
name

ten _____
name

111

Last song u
bought online?

What r your
screen names?

IM

What's your screensaver?

Do you blog?

○ nah ○ yeah

Blogs
I like

What do
u talk
about
in chat
rooms?

Fave Web site

cooles

of

year

it out

SHOP ONLINE?

○ nope ○ yep

coolest thing you've bought online?

...oogle the Most?

is the
site
I check
[ ] times
a week

My other fave
sites r:

2
3
4
5
6
7
8
9
10

How many hours
do u spend online
per week?

If you could create
it, what would be
the ULTIMATE
Web site?

back   next

113

THE Best OF THE BEST!

song _____

CD _____

movie _____

TV show _____

book _____

YouTube _____

junk food _____

friend _____

class _____

something someone said to me _____

_____

The Worst
of the worst!

song ....

CD ....

movie ....

TV show ....

book ....

YouTube ....

mistake ....

cafeteria food ....

class ....

something I said to someone ....

....

Place all your memories of this year here before taking on the next.

Save the Best 4 last!

My ___ grade year was
grade

○ ok ○ the worst ○ the best!

For the most part it was
- uneventful . . . let's just say I'm looking forward to next year.
- drama-filled – and I should know. I'm the queen of it!
  - unbelievably cool!
  - ugh! no words 2 describe it

It was the year of the

___
wardrobe item you wore the most

I hope I never HAVE to open another

___→
worst school subject ever

textbook again or I'll just die!
(at least I think so)

I'll never forget

___
___
___

best or worst memory

Details of a crush

_____
name

started off as the object of my affection. By the end of the year . . .

I ○ was still focusing on   ○ changed my focus to

_____
name

Really? How did it all turn out?

_____

_____

Events that Rocked my world!

life-changing, newsworthy, big stuff!

Major "me" events

me

the world

my town

Write a note to your future self . . .

_____

_____

What if

You could have **ONE** super power for 1 day . . .

Which power would you choose & what would you do with it?

☆ invisibility
☆ flight
☆ super strength
☆ other

Extra stuff!

Stick **anything** else that defines this year on these pages – **photos,** movie & concert tickets, notes – whatever u want.

Photo of you doing fave thing,
playing sports or hanging out w/pet

In PICTURES

Group shot of u & your BFFs
in favorite outfits

Close-up of you in fave
jeans or shoes

In Pictures

You in your bedroom
(it's more about your room than u)

Stick movie or concert
TICKET
here

_____
movie or concert
Who did u go w/?
_____
_____

It was ● Amazing ● OK ● Awful!

Stick movie or concert
TICKET
here

_____
movie or concert
Who did u go w/?
_____
_____

It was ● Amazing ● OK ● Awful!

Stick movie or concert
TICKET
here

_____
movie or concert
Who did u go w/?
_____
_____

It was ● Amazing ● OK ● Awful!

ment OF

_____
year

_____
movie or concert
Who did u go w/?
_____
_____

Stick movie or concert
TICKET
here

It was ● Amazing ● OK ● Awful!

_____
movie or concert
Who did u go w/?
_____
_____

Stick movie or concert
TICKET
here

It was ● Amazing ● OK ● Awful!

_____
movie or concert
Who did u go w/?
_____
_____

Stick movie or concert
TICKET
here

It was ● Amazing ● OK ● Awful!

_____
movie or concert

Who did u go w/?
_____
_____

It was ● Amazing ● OK ● Awful!

_____
movie or concert

Who did u go w/?
_____
_____

It was ● Amazing ● OK ● Awful!

_____
movie or concert

Who did u go w/?
_____
_____

It was ● Amazing ● OK ● Awful!

ment OF

_____ year

_____
movie or concert
Who did u go w/?
_____
_____

Stick movie or concert
TICKET
here

It was ● Amazing ● OK ● Awful!

_____
movie or concert
Who did u go w/?
_____
_____

Stick movie or concert
TICKET
here

It was ● Amazing ● OK ● Awful!

_____
movie or concert
Who did u go w/?
_____
_____

Stick movie or concert
TICKET
here

It was ● Amazing ● OK ● Awful!

Check out coke-or-pepsi.com

Take more quizzes
   Shop online for
       all of the
   Coke-or-Pepsi stuff!

coke
OR
pepsi?

Can you

it's 1 year

what R U

to do